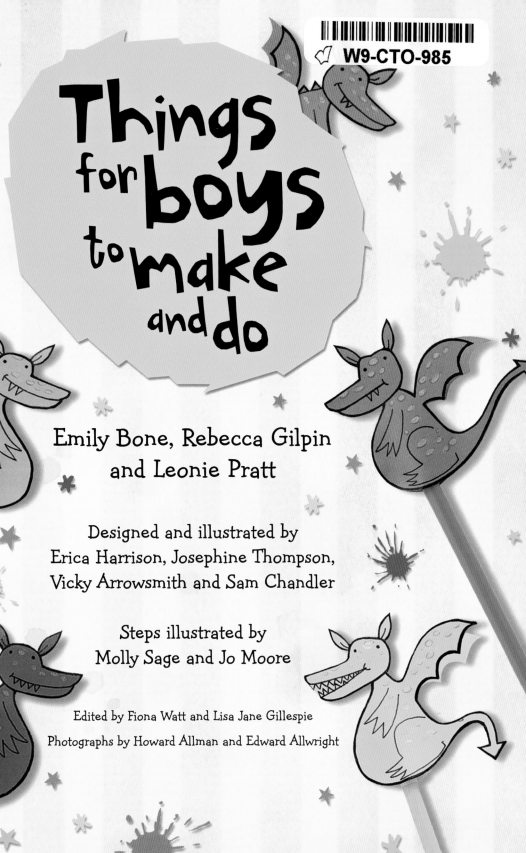

Things for boys to make and do

Emily Bone, Rebecca Gilpin
and Leonie Pratt

Designed and illustrated by
Erica Harrison, Josephine Thompson,
Vicky Arrowsmith and Sam Chandler

Steps illustrated by
Molly Sage and Jo Moore

Edited by Fiona Watt and Lisa Jane Gillespie
Photographs by Howard Allman and Edward Allwright

Contents

Bouncing bats

Scrunch the foil here.

1. Cut a rectangle from a roll of kitchen foil for the bat's body and head. Then, scrunch it tightly, about a third of the way along, like this.

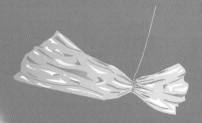

2. Cut a thin rubber band, to make a long piece for hanging the bat. Tie one end tightly around the scrunched part of the foil.

3. For the head, scrunch up the shorter end of the foil. As you scrunch the foil, bend it in on itself to where the rubber band is tied.

Make sure that the rubber band still sticks out of the middle.

4. Scrunch the other end of the foil in the same way, to make the body. Squeeze the head and body, to make them smooth and rounded.

Pull the rubber band out to one side.

5. Rip lots of small pieces of black tissue paper. Lay the bat on a piece of plastic foodwrap and brush part of it with white glue, like this.

6. Press pieces of tissue paper onto the wet glue. Then, brush on more glue and press on more tissue paper, until the bat is completely covered.

Fold

Fold the tabs
up, like this.

Hang up the
bat while the
glue dries.

7. Fold a strip of black paper in half, with the short ends together. Draw a wing shape against the fold, then, holding the layers together, cut it out.

8. Draw two ears on black paper, with a tab at the bottom. Cut out the ears, then glue their tabs. Glue the wings onto the bat, too.

9. Draw the bat's mouth with a silver pen. Then, draw eyes with black pupils, and fangs on white paper. Cut them out, then glue them onto the bat.

Gladiator fight

The fingers should look like they're gripping the sword.

Go over the outlines with a black pen.

1. Draw a gladiator's helmet near the top of a piece of thick white paper. Draw a long nose, then add the gladiator's eye, mouth, chin and neck.

2. Draw a circle for a shield, add the body and legs. Draw one arm reaching forward. Add small sausage shapes for the fingers and add a sword.

3. Add sandals and details on the clothes. Fill everything in using felt-tip pens. Cut out the gladiator, leaving a white border around the edge.

Make the gladiator 'fight' the lion by holding the handles and sliding them toward each other.

Gladiators were prisoners or slaves who were made to fight each other, or wild animals, to the death.

Glue each handle in the middle of the shapes.

4. Draw a lion's snout facing the other way from the gladiator. Add a snarling mouth, draw a mane around the top of the head. Add an eye and an ear.

5. Add the lion's front legs. Then, draw the body, and add back legs and a tail. Use felt-tip pens to fill in the lion, then cut it out, leaving a small border.

6. Cut two strips for handles from thick paper. Fold over one end of each handle, glue one onto the back of the lion, one onto the back of the gladiator.

You could make another gladiator to fight with, instead of a lion.

7. Cut a curved shape for an arena from pale paper. Glue it onto a big piece of cardboard. Cut another long strip from pale paper and fold under the ends.

Hook the gladiator and the lion over the strip.

8. Glue the ends of the strip onto the background, a little way up from the bottom. Slide the handles of the gladiator and lion under the strip.

Wild West painting

Use a pencil.

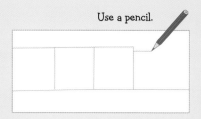

Leave a space here.

1. Draw a line all the way across a piece of thick paper, about a quarter of the way up. Then, draw four buildings above the line, like this.

2. Draw a sheriff, two barrels, some rocks and a snake in front of the buildings. Draw a walkway below the buildings, then add lines for boards.

3. To make a building into a jail, draw a door. Then, draw rectangles on either side of the door for windows and add crossing lines for bars.

Use the ideas on this page for buildings to draw in your town.

JAIL

Draw one window with the shutters open.

4. Draw a balcony halfway up the jail and add two poles down to the walkway. Then, draw four small windows with shutters above the balcony.

5. Add a star between the middle windows and a large sign above. Write 'JAIL' on the sign. Draw a prisoner looking out from one of the windows.

6. Draw the rest of the buildings. Fill in your picture using watery paints. When the paint is dry, go over all the lines using a thin black pen.

Ancient treasure map

1. To make a piece of white paper look old, rip little strips from around its edges. Tightly crumple the paper and then open it out again.

The tea will make the paper turn brown.

2. Pour some cold, strong tea into a dish. Lower the paper into the tea and push it down, so that the tea covers it completely.

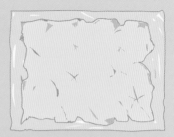

3. Leave the paper to soak for about an hour. Then, carefully lift it out and lay it on a piece of plastic foodwrap until it is totally dry.

You could draw a map with lots of small islands instead of one big one.

4. Draw a big wiggly shape, for a treasure island. Then, draw a pirate ship, and some waves for a stormy sea, near the top of the map.

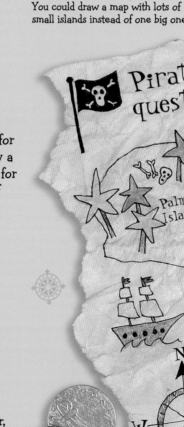

Pirate Pete's quest for gold

Palm Tree Island

Turtle Island

Treasure Island

N

W   E

S

5. Draw a flag and write 'TREASURE MAP' beside it. Add a compass in one corner, then draw some rocks around the island.

TREASURE MAP

Dead Man's Cave

Quicksand

Misty Mountains

Rugged Rascal Rocks

Shark-Infested Sea

Crocodile Swamp

Snake Forest

N
W   E
S

Look at the photo for different ideas.

TREASURE MAP

6. Add waves and sharks' fins, for a shark-infested sea. Then, on the island, draw lots of dangers and write names next to them.

7. Fill in your picture with pencils. Then, mark where the treasure is hidden with a red 'X' and draw a dotted line from the ship to the 'X'.

Casting a magic spell

1. Using a pencil, carefully draw a curved line for the wizard's nose, near the top of a piece of white paper. Then, add two dots for his eyes.

Draw lots of lines, like this.

2. Starting at the top of the nose, draw a tall, pointed hat, like this. Add the wizard's whiskers and beard, then draw his long hair.

3. Draw a big triangle with a curve at the bottom for the wizard's robe. Add two lines in the middle of the robe for his gown.

4. Draw two long triangles for the robe's flowing sleeves. Then, add the wizard's hands, and a line for his wand coming from one of them.

Use pale blue paint for the hair, whiskers and beard.

5. Using watery paints, carefully paint the wizard's face, hands, hair, whiskers and beard. Then, paint his robe and gown, too.

6. Leave the paint to dry completely. Then, carefully draw over all the pencil outlines with a thin black felt-tip pen.

Sprinkle wet glue with glitter, if you don't have glitter glue.

7. Using gold glitter glue, draw lines along the edges of the wizard's robe, his sleeves and the bottom of his hat. Add lots of spots, too.

8. Draw gold and purple glitter glue swirls coming from the wand. Smudge some of the swirls a little, with the tip of your finger.

Add star sequins to the wizard's robe.

9. While the glitter glue is still wet, press on some star sequins. Press one onto the end of his wand, and glue some onto his gown, too.

Egyptian mummy

1. For a mummy's head, scrunch up a piece of kitchen foil into a tight ball. Then, scrunch up a larger piece into a sausage shape for a body.

2. Scrunch up four thin sausage shapes about the length of the body for arms and legs. Then, roll a small foil shape for the mummy's feet.

Press the foil around the body parts as you wrap.

3. Arrange the parts of the mummy in the middle of a large piece of kitchen foil, like this. Carefully wrap the foil around them to hold them together.

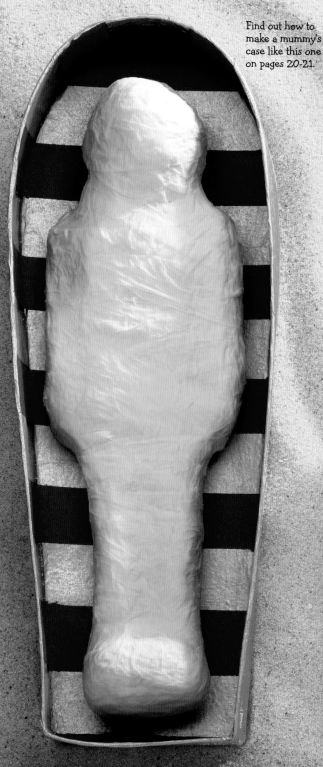

Find out how to make a mummy's case like this one on pages 20-21.

4. Rip some paper towels into about 20 strips that are about the width of your finger. Soak the strips in a dish of water until they are totally wet.

5. Lay the mummy on plastic foodwrap. Then, take a strip of paper towel out of the water and wrap it around the body and arms like a bandage.

6. Wrap another strip around the mummy. Continue to wrap overlapping strips around the mummy until the foil is completely covered.

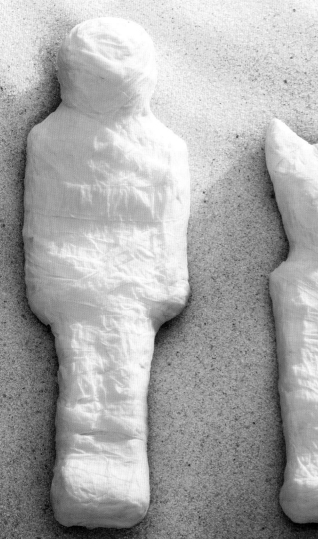

7. When the mummy is dry, brush white glue all over the bandages to secure them. Lay the mummy on the plastic foodwrap until the glue is dry.

When an important Egyptian person died, they were mummified. Their insides were removed, then their body was dried out and wrapped in bandages. The mummy was then put in a case and buried. Egyptians also mummified animals, including cats, dogs and crocodiles.

Sheriff collage

'Bowed' legs curve out, like this.

1. Draw a cowboy's bowed legs on a picture of blue jeans from an old magazine. Cut out the legs and glue them near the bottom of a piece of paper.

2. Draw two cowboy boots on brown paper and cut them out. Draw a shirt and cut it out, too. Then, glue the shapes onto the paper, like this.

3. Cut out two rectangles and glue them onto the shirt. Draw a star-shaped sheriff's badge on yellow paper. Cut it out and glue it onto the cowboy's body.

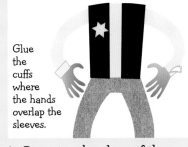

Glue the cuffs where the hands overlap the sleeves.

4. Draw two hands as if they are about to grab something. Cut them out and glue them onto the arms. Cut out cuffs and glue them onto the hands.

5. Cut out a head, nose and white circles for eyes, glue them on. Cut out some hair and a hat, and glue them onto the cowboy's head.

6. Cut two holsters from paper and glue them onto the jeans. Then, use a black pen to draw eyebrows, a mouth and dots in the cowboy's eyes.

To make a showdown scene like this one, make a background from paper first, then glue on two cowboys – a sheriff and an outlaw.

This cowboy's shirt was cut from a picture of a shirt in a magazine.

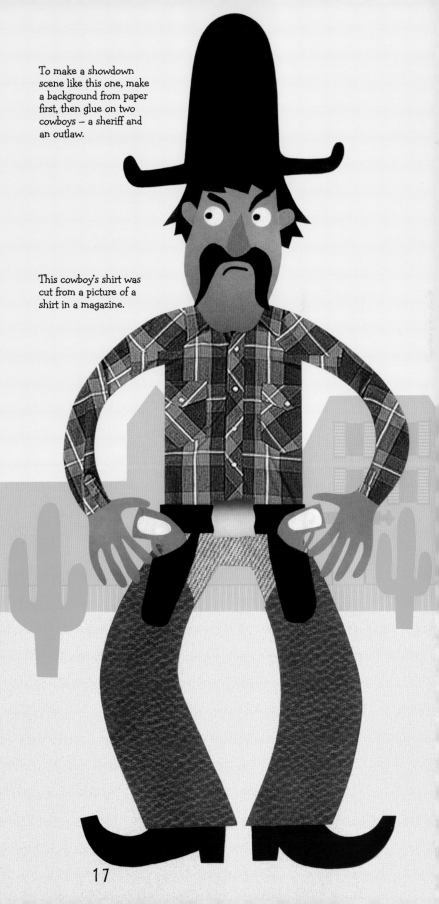

17

Monster bookmark

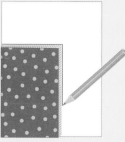

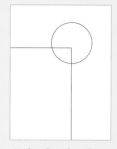

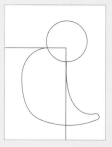

1. Lay a book on the bottom left-hand corner of a piece of thick white paper. Draw around it carefully with a pencil, pressing lightly.

2. Lift off the book. Then, draw a circle for the head of the monster over the top right-hand corner of this rectangle, like this.

3. Draw a shape for the monster's body, following the top and right-hand side of the rectangle. Then, add a pointed tail at the bottom.

To make your monster grip onto a book, slide him between the pages, leaving his hands outside.

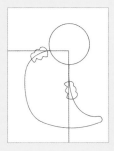  

4. Draw a hand at the top of the body, near the head. Make it overlap the body. Then, add another hand above the tail, like this.

5. Erase the rectangle and any lines inside the monster's hands. Draw the monster's face and horns, and add a big oval for the tummy.

6. Draw spots on the body and head. Add stripes on the horns, and fins on the back, too. Then, fill in the monster with thick paints.

To make a bookmark like this one, just cut around one hand.

7. When the paint is dry, draw over all the lines and around the spots with a black felt-tip pen. Then, cut out the monster.

Make sure you don't cut off the monster's hands completely.

8. To make your monster into a bookmark, carefully cut part of the way around each of the hands, along the red lines shown here.

Mummy case

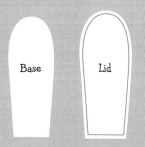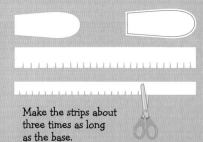

Base

Lid

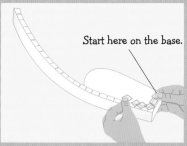

Make the strips about three times as long as the base.

Start here on the base.

1. Draw a base for a mummy case on thin cardboard. Cut it out and lay it on another piece of cardboard. Draw around it, cut it out leaving a thin border.

2. Cut a long strip of cardboard for the sides of the base. Cut a slightly thinner strip for the lid. Make flaps by cutting slits along one edge of each strip.

3. Fold over all the flaps on both strips. Hold the wider strip against the base and fold the flaps over it. Tape the first few flaps onto the base, like this.

Egyptian mummies were kept in painted cases that were covered in pictures and hieroglyphic writing. The person painted on each case was a picture of the man or woman inside. You'll find hieroglyphic letters to copy on page 57.

4. Bend the strip all around the base, securing the flaps with tape. Trim off any extra cardboard, tape around the corner where the ends meet.

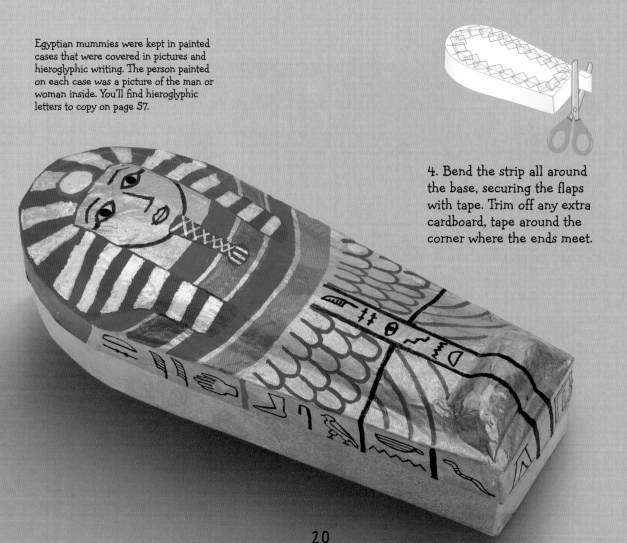

The tissue paper makes the lid look 3-D.

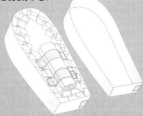

5. Follow steps 3-4 to attach the thinner strip to the lid in the same way. Roll some tissue paper into a long shape for legs. Tape it onto the lid, like this.

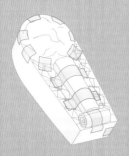

6. Roll some more tissue paper into a ball, then press it down to flatten it. Tape it onto the lid for a head. Then, tape on a small roll of tissue paper for feet.

Find out how to make a mummy to put inside your case on pages 14-15.

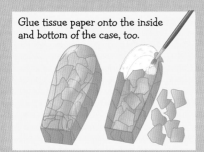

Glue tissue paper onto the inside and bottom of the case, too.

7. Rip up pieces of gold tissue paper. Brush white glue on part of the lid and press on the pieces of paper. Continue like this until the whole case is covered.

Use a thin paintbrush and black paint if you don't have a pen with permanent ink.

8. When the glue is dry, use a black felt-tip pen with permanent ink to draw a face. Draw a shape for a headdress and fill it in with black paint.

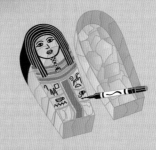

9. Decorate the lid using red and green paint. When the paint is dry, add stripes on the headdress using a gold pen. Use the black pen to add hieroglyphics.

Siege painting

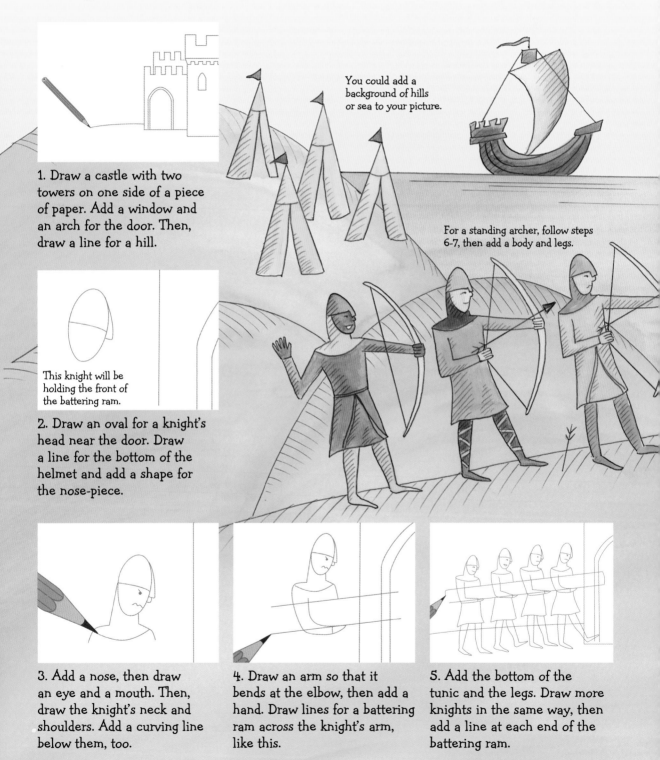

1. Draw a castle with two towers on one side of a piece of paper. Add a window and an arch for the door. Then, draw a line for a hill.

This knight will be holding the front of the battering ram.

2. Draw an oval for a knight's head near the door. Draw a line for the bottom of the helmet and add a shape for the nose-piece.

You could add a background of hills or sea to your picture.

For a standing archer, follow steps 6-7, then add a body and legs.

3. Add a nose, then draw an eye and a mouth. Then, draw the knight's neck and shoulders. Add a curving line below them, too.

4. Draw an arm so that it bends at the elbow, then add a hand. Draw lines for a battering ram across the knight's arm, like this.

5. Add the bottom of the tunic and the legs. Draw more knights in the same way, then add a line at each end of the battering ram.

Add more knights
in the battlements
shooting arrows
at the enemy.

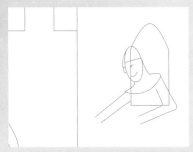

6. For an archer, draw the head, neck and shoulders of a knight in the window. Then, add the arms, with one straight and one bent.

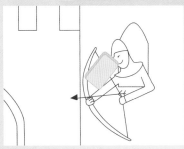

7. Draw hands, a bow and arrow, add fingers on the hand holding the bow. Erase the extra pencil lines and go over the outlines with a ballpoint pen.

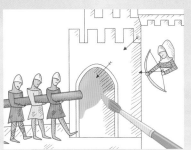

8. Add lines on all the knights and the castle, for shading. Then, fill in all of your picture using different shades of watery paint.

Penalty shoot-out game

Make the strip the width of the two rectangles.

1. Cut two rectangles of thin cardboard that are the same size, one white and one green. Then, cut a long strip of thick cardboard, about 3cm (1in) wide.

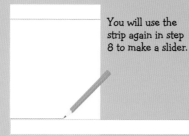

You will use the strip again in step 8 to make a slider.

2. Fold the white rectangle in half, then unfold it again. Lay the cardboard strip along the top and draw along it, then draw a line at the bottom, too.

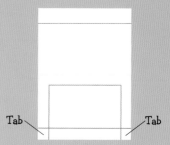

Tab   Tab

3. Draw a goal in the bottom half of the cardboard, across the line, like this. The little squares below the line will be tabs for the goal's base.

Play this game with a friend. Take it in turns to be the goalkeeper or the penalty-taker.

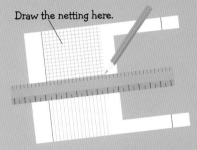
Draw the netting here.

Fold the tabs before you glue them onto the base.

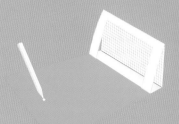

4. Cut out the goal. Then, use a ruler and a blue pencil to draw lots of lines for netting. Draw them between the top line from step 2 and the middle fold.

5. To make the goal, fold the cardboard along the top line from step 2 to make a base. Then, fold the goal in half and glue the tabs onto the base.

6. Spread glue along one end of the green rectangle, then press the goal onto the glue. Using a white pencil, draw a penalty spot.

Glue the stand in the middle of the slider.

Glue the front flap under here.

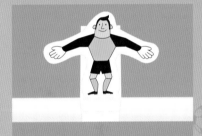

7. To make a stand for the goalkeeper, cut a strip of thick paper that is a little taller than the goal. Fold it in half, then fold up the bottom to make flaps.

8. Unfold the flaps, then open the paper a little. Glue the back flap to the bottom of the slider from step 2. Then, fold the front back and glue its flap on, too.

9. Draw a goalkeeper on a separate piece of paper. Fill him in with felt-tip pens and cut around him. Then, glue the goalkeeper onto the stand.

Before you play the game, secure the corners of the green paper with little balls of poster tack.

10. Fold up the ends of the slider. Slide it between the goal posts and the netting. Make a ball from a piece of foil and place it on the penalty spot.

How to play (2 players):
One player tries to score a penalty by flicking the ball at the goal. The other player tries to block the shot by moving the goalkeeper from side to side with the slider.

Move the slider with your thumbs.

Pirate money bags

Silver coins

The lid of a spice jar is ideal.

1. To make a silver coin, lay the lid of a small jar on a piece of thin cardboard and draw around it twice. Then, cut out the circles.

Glue the circles onto the non-shiny side.

2. Glue the circles onto a piece of kitchen foil. Then, cut around them, leaving a border. Bend the foil over the edges of the circles.

Be careful not to tear the foil.

3. Using a blunt pencil, draw dots around the edge of each circle. Draw a picture in the middle. Then, glue the circles firmly together.

You could make gold coins from a chocolate wrapper.

To make different-sized coins, use more than one size of lid.

Drawstring money bags

1. Fold a long piece of crêpe paper in half, then open it out. Carefully, spread glue along the longer edges of one half, like this.

2. Fold the paper in half again, making sure that the edges line up, like this. Press the edges together, then leave the glue to dry.

The hole goes through all the layers.

3. Fold the bag in half lengthways, twice. Using one side of a hole puncher, make a hole a third of the way down the bag.

4. Draw a skull and four bones on a piece of paper and carefully cut them out. Draw a face on the skull, then glue the shapes onto the bag.

5. Thread a long piece of ribbon in and out of the holes around the bag. Fill the bag with coins, then tie the ends of the ribbon.

Cowboy hat

1. To make the hat band, cut a wide strip of thin cardboard, long enough to fit around your head with a little overlap. Tape the ends to secure them.

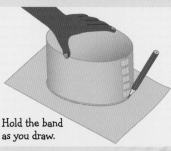

Hold the band as you draw.

2. Take the band off your head, then gently press the sides together a little to make an oval. Place it on some thin cardboard and draw around it.

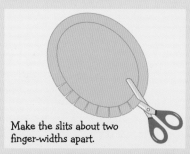

Make the slits about two finger-widths apart.

3. Draw a bigger oval around the first one. Cut around the big oval. Make flaps by cutting lots of slits in from the edge of the cardboard to the smaller oval.

4. Fold up the flaps around the edge of the oval. Then, gently slot the oval inside the hat band, making sure that all the flaps are pointing up.

Learn how to make a sheriff's badge on page 82.

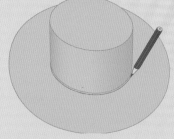

5. Carefully push the oval down into the hat band, all the way to the bottom. Use lots of pieces of sticky tape to secure all of the flaps.

6. For the brim, cut out a big circle from cardboard. Place the hat band in the middle of the circle and draw around it. Then, lift it off.

7. Draw a smaller oval inside the one you have just drawn. Gently bend the cardboard in half and hold it in the middle. Cut around the smaller oval.

8. Make flaps by cutting slits all the way around the inside of the brim, up to the line of the bigger oval you drew in step 6. Fold all the flaps over.

9. To attach the brim, lay the hat band upside down. Then, slot the flaps on the brim into the hat band. Tape the flaps to the inside of the band.

10. Turn the hat the correct way up. Cut a long piece of ribbon and tie it around the hat band. Then, bend the opposite sides of the brim up, like this.

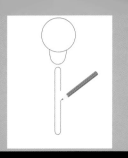

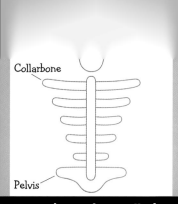

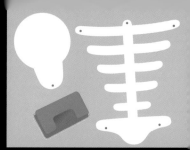

1. Lay a small plate near the top of a large piece of cardboard and draw around it. Add a jaw below the circle, then draw a long spine.

2. Draw shapes for a collarbone a little way down from the top of the spine. Add four ribs below the collarbone, and a pelvis at the bottom, like this.

3. Cut around the outline of the shapes. Using a hole puncher, make holes in the skull, spine, collarbone and pelvis, shown by the red dots above.

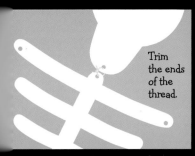

Trim the ends of the thread.

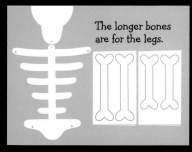

The longer bones are for the legs.

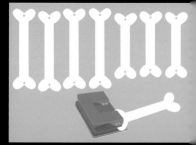

4. To join the head and body, cut a piece of white thread. Push it through the hole in the bottom of the skull and the hole in the spine, then knot it.

5. Fold two pieces of thin white cardboard in half. On one, draw two bones about the length of the spine. On the other piece, draw two shorter bones.

6. Keeping the cardboard folded, cut around the bones, to make four long bones and four shorter ones. Punch holes near the ends of all the bones.

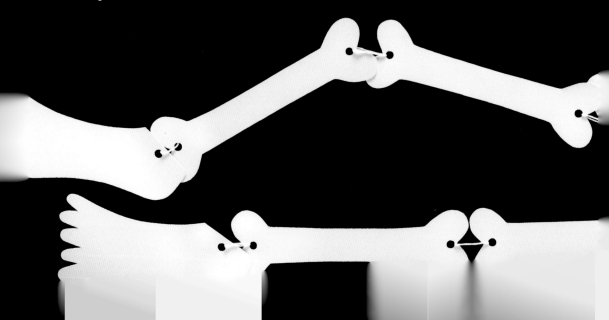

You can move
your skeleton's
arms and legs into
lots of different
positions.

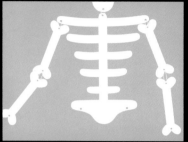

7. To make the arms, join two
of the shorter bones with a
piece of thread, as before. Join
the other two short bones. Join
both arms onto the collarbone.

Make a hole where
each red dot is shown.

8. Join the long bones to make
legs and join them onto the
pelvis. Draw hands and feet on
scraps of cardboard, cut them
out and punch holes in them.

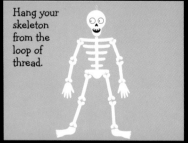

Hang your
skeleton
from the
loop of
thread.

9. Join the hands and feet onto
the arms and legs. Using a black
felt-tip pen, draw a face on the
skull. Tape a loop of thread onto
the back of the skull.

31

Pirate flags

Cut shapes from foil, like the sword below.

1. For the flags, fold several narrow rectangles of bright paper in half, with their short ends together. Crease each fold really well.

You could draw stripes on some of the flags with a felt-tip pen.

2. With the fold at the top, draw an upside-down 'V' at the bottom of each flag. Then, carefully cut along these lines, keeping the layers together.

3. Draw skulls and bones, anchors, flags and palm trees on pieces of paper. Cut out the shapes and glue them onto the flags.

The glue stops the flags from sliding along the thread.

4. Open out the flags and spread glue along the folds. Fold the flags over a long piece of thread and press the glued parts together.

Dragon pencil top

1. Draw a dragon's head on a piece of paper. Add a rounded body, a wing and a tail. Cut out the dragon, then erase the pencil lines.

2. Lay this dragon down on the paper again and carefully draw around it. Then, cut around the second dragon, along the outline.

The dragon shapes need to face each other.

3. Outline the dragons with a black felt-tip pen. Draw their arms and legs. Add a face on one of them, then add spots with a pencil, too.

4. Cut a strip of paper and roll it around the end of a pencil. Secure it with tape, then tape it to the back of one of the dragons.

Bend the wings out a little.

5. Spread glue all over the dragon, except for its wings. Press the other dragon on top and hold them together until the glue sticks.

Egyptian tomb picture

This will be the man's body and skirt.

1. Using a pencil, draw a triangle on a piece of white paper. Draw an upside-down triangle overlapping the first one. Erase where the triangles overlap.

2. Draw an oval above the body for a head and add lines for a neck. Draw a nose and chin on one side of the head. Add hair on the other side.

3. Draw two legs below the body, and add two feet pointing to one side. Draw a slanting line across the middle of the man's body to make a skirt.

For a servant carrying a stick, draw his arm bending across his body.

The cracked wax effect makes the picture look like an old tomb painting.

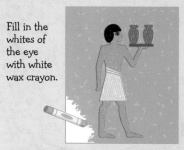

4. Add an arm that bends up in a V-shape coming out from one side of the body, like this. Then, draw a flat hand at the end of the arm.

5. Draw a thin rectangle for a flat tray on top of the hand, then draw two pots on top of it. Add a straight arm on the other side of the man's body.

Fill in the whites of the eye with white wax crayon.

6. Use a black wax crayon to draw an eye and eyebrow on the face, and fill in the hair. Fill in the rest of the picture and background using wax crayons.

Make sure you brush paint into all the creases.

7. Scrunch up the paper into a tight ball. Carefully open the paper out again and flatten it. Then, brush dark blue paint all over the picture, like this.

For a serving girl, draw longer hair and a long dress. Draw lots of patterns on the dress and fill them in with wax crayons.

8. Rinse the paper under cold running water. Rub it gently with your hand until you can see the picture again. Lay the paper on plastic foodwrap to dry.

The walls inside a pyramid were often decorated with paintings of scenes from everyday life. The Egyptians painted people with their heads and feet turned to one side. This picture shows servants carrying food to a banquet.

Fighting knights

Add sequins or stickers for a pair of spurs.

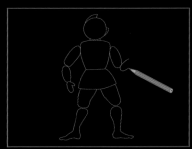

1. Draw a circle for a knight's head, then add a crest on top and a visor on one side. Draw a shape for the body, then add the arms and the legs.

2. Use thick white paint to fill in the knight. Then, when the paint is dry, use a red chalk or a chalk pastel to draw a plume on the top of the helmet.

Make one piece from each half a little bigger than the others.

3. Draw a circle on some foil to make joints for the elbows, shoulders and knees. Cut out the circle, then cut it in half. Cut each half into three parts.

Knights followed a 'code of chivalry'. This meant they had to behave well at all times – even when they were fighting.

Draw circles with the glitter glue to get a chain mail effect, like on this knight.

4. Glue the bigger pieces on the knight's shoulders and the other pieces on his knees and elbows. Then, glue sequins on each joint and on the helmet.

5. Decorate the helmet and the bottom of the body using a silver pen. Then, draw curly patterns on the arms and legs using silver glitter glue.

6. Use sequins and shapes cut from shiny paper to decorate the knight's body. Then, carefully cut out a sword and glue it onto one of his hands.

37

Pirate ship card

Fold

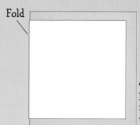

Slide the paper in as far as the fold.

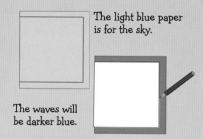

The light blue paper is for the sky.

The waves will be darker blue.

Draw the line near the bottom of the paper.

1. Fold a long rectangle of thick paper in half, with its short ends together. Then, slide a piece of light blue paper inside the card.

2. Draw around the front of the card. Then, slide a piece of darker blue paper into the card and carefully draw around it, too.

3. Cut out the blue shapes. Glue the light blue shape inside the card. Then, draw a long, wavy line across the dark blue shape.

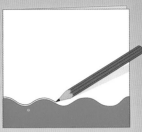

To make a desert island card like this, make a tall, thin card in step 1.

4. Fold the card again. Then, cut along the wavy line and lay the waves on the card. Draw along the top edge of the waves.

5. Draw a pirate's ship with tall masts, big sails and fluttering flags, overlapping the wavy line. Then, go over the lines with a black felt-tip pen.

Use a pen that matches the paper inside the card.

6. Fill in the ship with felt-tip pens. Add some pale blue sky between the sails and around the ship, but don't fill in the waves or the sea.

Leave a border of sky around the edge of the ship.

7. To cut out the ship, cut down the fold, as far as the waves. Cut along the waves on both sides of the ship, and around the sky.

8. Glue the dark blue wave shape onto the card. Then, cut shapes for little waves and glue them on. Glue paper clouds onto the sky, too.

Roman soldier paperchain

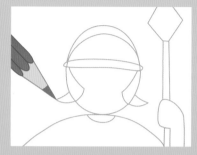

1. Fold a paper rectangle in half, then in half again. Draw a head and shoulders, then add a curve for the neck. Add a shield, touching the fold, too.

2. Draw a spear. Add a hand holding the spear so that the arm is close to the fold, like this. Draw the soldier's tunic, then add the legs and feet.

3. For the helmet, draw a rim across the head. Add a curve for the top, draw two cheek guards. Then, draw curves on either side of the head.

The soldiers with feathers on their helmets are called centurions. They also wore metal leg protectors.

Adding shapes to the plates makes them look as if they are overlapping.

Don't cut around the folds, marked here in red.

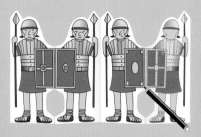

4. Draw a belt and some plates across the middle of the soldier's body. Then, add lines for shoulder plates. Draw shapes at the top of the plates.

5. Keeping the paper folded, cut around the soldier through all the layers of paper. Don't cut the folds near the shield and spear. Unfold the paper.

6. Draw more Roman soldiers with shields and spears inside the other shapes. Fill them in using pencils. Then, use a black pen to draw outlines and faces.

The Romans' large and well-trained army allowed them to take over most of Europe and parts of Africa and Asia.

Stained glass window

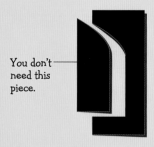

You don't need this piece.

1. Fold a piece of black paper in half. Draw half an arch against the fold, for a window. Then, keeping the paper folded, cut out the arch.

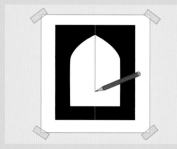

2. Tape a piece of white paper onto a work surface. Unfold the window and lay it on top, then draw a line down the middle of the arch.

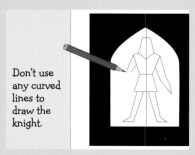

Don't use any curved lines to draw the knight.

3. Draw shapes for a knight's helmet and body at the top of the arch. Add the legs, then draw one bent arm and the top of the other arm.

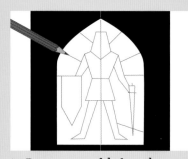

4. Draw a sword below the bent arm and a shield below the other arm. Then, add lines coming out from the knight to the very edge of the arch.

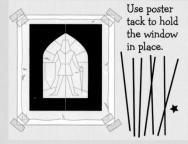

Use poster tack to hold the window in place.

5. Lay a big piece of plastic foodwrap over your drawing and lay the window on top. Then, cut lots of thin strips and a star from black paper.

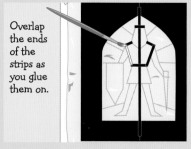

Overlap the ends of the strips as you glue them on.

6. Brush white glue down the middle of the arch and press a strip on top. Cut all the strips to fit over the lines in your drawing and glue them on.

Keep one blob white.

7. For the 'stained glass', squeeze several blobs of white glue onto an old plate. Then, mix a different shade of food dye into each blob of glue.

8. Brush a thick layer of yellow glue around the knight. Then, brush orange glue from the yellow out to the edge of the arch, like this.

Put the knight against a window so that light shines through it.

9. Use green glue at the bottom, then fill in the knight with other shades. Leave the glue to dry overnight, then peel off the foodwrap.

Overhead kick door sign

Hook this part of the door sign over a door handle.

TOM'S
ROOM

1. Draw around a large roll of sticky tape near the top of a piece of thick paper. Draw two lines down to the bottom of the paper, then cut out the shape.

Don't worry if the strips go over the edges.

2. Turn the shape over. Rip strips from wrapping paper or paper from old magazines. Glue them across the shape, then let the glue dry.

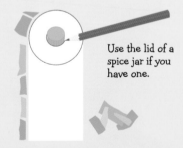

Use the lid of a spice jar if you have one.

3. Turn the paper shape over again and trim around the edges. Then, lay the lid from a small jar in the middle of the circle and draw around it.

MICHAEL'S ROOM

4. To make the paper shape into a door sign, draw two curving lines (shown here in red). Then, cut along the lines and around the small circle.

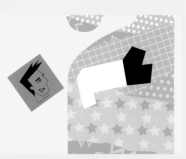

Shirt — Shorts

5. Turn the door sign over. Then, draw a shirt and a pair of shorts on scraps of paper. Cut them out and glue them onto the door sign, like this.

You could make a sign that you can press onto your door with poster tack instead.

6. Draw a head and neck on another piece of paper. Cut out the shape, then glue it on so that it overlaps the neck and the edge of the door sign.

Glue the boots on before the socks.

7. Draw an arm and two legs on some paper. Cut them out and glue them on. Cut out shapes for socks and boots, and glue them on, too.

You could draw stripes or other details on the shirt, too.

TOM'S ROOM

8. Cut out a ball and glue it on. Glue on thin strips of paper beside it as movement lines. Then, write your name on the sign with a black pen.

Wild West 'WANTED' poster

If you don't have a digital photo, you could glue a photograph of yourself onto the paper after step 4.

Carefully, stir the mixture so that the water turns dark brown.

1. Print a black and white digital photo of yourself onto white paper. Tear strips from the edges of the paper. Crumple it up and open it out again.

2. To stain the paper, put four teabags into a container. Boil water in a kettle, then carefully pour the water over the tea bags. Leave the tea to cool.

3. Lay the paper in a wide, shallow dish. Pour the cold tea over the paper so that the paper is completely covered. Then, remove the tea bags.

4. Leave the paper to soak for at least an hour. Then, take the paper out of the tea and lay it on a piece of plastic foodwrap until it is completely dry.

5. Write 'WANTED' at the top of your poster and an outlaw name. Below your photo, write 'Reward' and '$150,000'. Fill in the words using a felt-tip pen.

WANTED
Buffalo Bob

Reward
$150 000

WANTED

Horse Rustler Hank

$100 000

WANTED

DEAD OR ALIVE

REWARD

$100 000

You could put on an outlaw outfit then take a photo for your poster.

6. To make yourself look like a Wild West outlaw, draw a cowboy hat on a piece of brown paper. Cut it out, then glue it onto your photo.

7. Draw a bandana on patterned paper. Cut it out and glue it onto the neck. Cut out drooping whiskers from black paper and glue them onto the face.

Wizard store

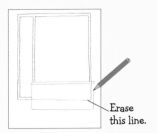
Erase this line.

1. Draw a shape for the store's shelving on a piece of white paper. Then, add a shop counter overlapping the shelving, like this.

2. Draw a wizard's pointy hat above the counter. Add his face and beard, and then draw his body. Draw piles of coins in front of him.

3. Draw a ladder at one end of the counter. Add a book of spells on a book rest, and a cash register, next to the wizard, too.

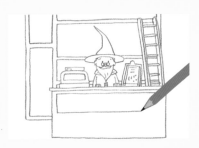

4. Draw several shelves on the shelving behind the wizard. Then, draw a display window on the front of the shop counter, like this.

5. Draw a clothes stand next to the counter. Add a wizard's cat and lots of different sized cauldrons in front of the counter, too.

6. Add a 'Wizard Supplies Ltd.' sign above the cat. Draw some cushions inside the window display, with magic wands and quills on them.

7. Draw lots of wizard supplies arranged on the shelves, looking at the big picture opposite for ideas. Add some mice and spiders.

8. Using a thin paintbrush, carefully fill in the wizard with runny paints. Then, paint the rest of the picture and leave the paint to dry.

9. Draw over all the pencil lines with a thin black felt-tip pen. Then, write made-up names on the labels on the jars and boxes, too.

Small   Medium   Large

Ink   Ink
Ink   Ink
Ink   Ink

Silver – Small

Gold – Medium   Silver – Medium

Black – Medium   Navy – Medium

Navy – Large   Black – Large

Slimy stuff

Gruesome green gloop

The Usborne Book of Spells

Wizard Supplies Ltd.

Monster mask

1. Draw a large egg shape for the monster's head on a big piece of thick paper. Make the shape wider and taller than your own head.

2. Draw a wide curving mouth halfway down the monster's head. Add two pointed ears and two little bumps near the top, like this.

3. Cut out the monster's head. Then, carefully push the point of a ballpoint pen through the middle of the mouth, gently, to make a hole.

4. Carefully, push one blade of a pair of scissors through the hole. Cut to the edge of the mouth, then cut all the way around it.

Cut through all the layers.

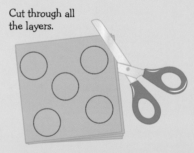

5. Fold a piece of paper in half. Fold it in half again, then draw five spots on it. Cut out the spots and glue them all over the mask.

This is the back of the mask.

6. Draw large rounded teeth on white paper and cut them out. Turn the mask over, then glue the teeth around the mouth, like this.

7. Draw two big eyes on paper and cut them out. Then, cut two long strips of thick paper and fold over one end of each one, like this.

8. Fold the strips one way and then the other way to make zigzags. Glue an eye onto each one, then glue the other ends onto the mask.

Tape the band a little way above the mouth.

9. Cut a thick paper band that fits around your head, with a little overlap. Tape the ends, together and then tape it onto the back of the mask.

You can't see the zigzag springs in this photograph, but they will make the eyes bounce around when you wear your mask.

To wear your mask, slide the band onto your head and look out through the mouth.

You could make monster hands to wear with your mask (see pages 84-85).

Cowboy sunset painting

1. To make a sunset sky, pour some thick yellow paint onto an old plate. Pour thick orange and red paints onto the plate, too. Spread them out a little.

2. Dip a large paintbrush into the yellow paint. Then, paint a thick strip at the bottom of a white piece of paper, covering about half of the page.

3. Without washing your brush, dip it into the orange paint. Then, paint a thinner orange strip so that it blends into the yellow paint, like this.

4. Paint the top part of the paper red in the same way. When the paint is dry, use a pencil to draw a line across the paper for the horizon.

5. For a rearing horse, draw a large, slanting oval for the body above the horizon, like this. Draw a smaller oval for the head and a shape for the nose.

6. Add ears on the horse's head and two curved lines for the neck. Then, draw two legs at the back of the horse that go down to the horizon.

7. Draw two bent legs at the front of the horse. Add a mane and a tail. Draw a cowboy's body on the horse's back, add his head with an open mouth.

8. Draw a hat on top of the head, then draw a triangle for the cowboy's nose and add some hair. Draw a pointed boot under the horse's body.

9. Add a curved arm and one touching the horse's neck, too. Use thick black paint to fill in the horse, cowboy and area below the horizon.

You could make your picture look like a Wild West desert by drawing rocks and cacti on the horizon.

Spooky full-moon collage

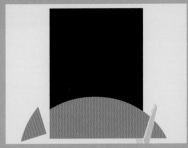

Use a blue chalk if you don't have a chalk pastel.

The chalk dust gives the white paper a moon-like texture.

1. Cut a curved shape for a hill from purple paper and glue it at the bottom of a large piece of black paper. Then, trim the sides that overlap the edges.

2. For the moon, draw around a bowl on white paper, cut out the circle. Make blue chalk dust by scribbling hard with a chalk pastel on a scrap of paper.

3. Scrunch up a small piece of tissue paper. Dip it into the chalk dust, then dab it over the paper moon. Glue the moon onto the black paper, above the hill.

4. Using a pencil, draw a curving tree with branches and leaves on blue paper. Draw a second tree on purple paper, then cut out both trees.

5. Glue on the trees so that they overlap the moon and hill. Leave a space for houses in the middle. Trim off any parts of the trees overlapping the edges.

6. Draw some wonky rectangles and funny shapes for houses on scraps of blue and purple paper. Cut them out, then glue them along the top of the hill.

7. Cut triangles for roofs from scraps of paper and cardboard and glue them on. Then, draw sinister faces on the blue tree and the houses.

8. Using a pencil, draw spooky monsters and bats on pieces of black paper. Cut them all out, then glue the monsters on the hill, and the bats on the moon.

9. Draw four round eyes and two speech bubbles on scraps of paper. Cut them all out and glue them onto the picture. Write monster talk in the bubbles.

Roman scroll

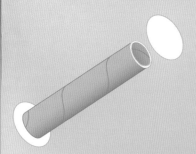
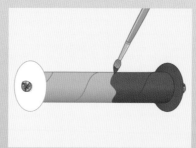

1. Lay a cup on thin cardboard. Draw around it twice. Cut out the circles. Brush glue on the ends of a tube from a paper towel roll. Press on the circles.

2. Cut two pieces of tissue paper. Dip them in glue, roll each one into a ball. Press them onto the ends of the scroll. Let the glue dry. Paint the scroll.

3. When the paint is dry, cut a rectangle of paper that is nearly as wide as the cardboard tube. Tape the paper on and wrap it around the scroll.

I = 1	II = 2	III = 3	IV = 4
V = 5	VI = 6	VII = 7	VIII = 8
IX = 9	X = 10	XI = 11	XII = 12
L = 50	C = 100	D = 500	M = 1,000

The symbols on this scroll are Roman numerals. Romans used these in the same way we use numbers today.

Romans wrote things on scrolls instead of books. A scroll was kept rolled up until someone wanted to read what was on it.

You could tie a ribbon around your scroll to secure it when it's rolled up.

Hieroglyphics

Egyptian writing was made up of painted pictures called hieroglyphs. In Ancient Egypt, each picture stood for a letter, a sound or a whole word. Here are examples of hieroglyphs that you can use to write messages or decorate the things you make.

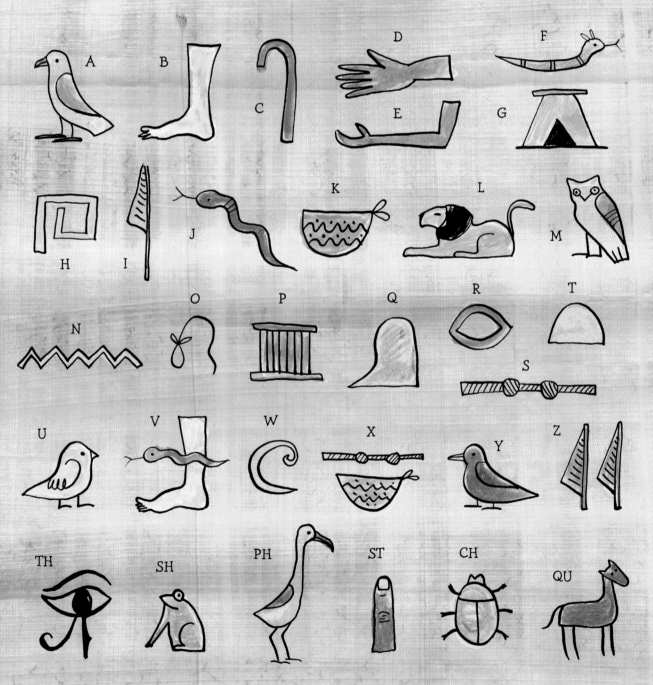

Cowboy belt

1. To make a belt, cut out a long strip of thin brown cardboard. The belt should be long enough to fit around your hips with a little overlap.

This will look like the end of the belt.

2. Cut a shorter strip that is the same width as the belt. Cut off the corners from one end to make a point. Glue the other end onto the middle of the belt.

You could glue on more tiny circles for extra decoration.

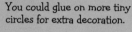

3. For a buckle, cut an oval from cardboard. Cut out a small circle and a star. Glue the circle in the middle of the oval, glue the star onto the circle.

4. Cut a piece of string that fits around the buckle. Glue the string just inside the edge of the buckle. When the glue is dry, paint the buckle gold.

Don't cover this end.

5. When the paint is dry, spread glue over the back of the buckle. Press it onto the middle of the belt, covering the end of the strip you glued on earlier.

Glue the loop so it looks like it is holding the end of the belt in place.

6. Cut a thin strip from cardboard for a belt loop. Lay it a little away from the buckle, fold the ends around and glue them onto the back of the belt.

Don't cut along the fold.

7. For a holster, fold a rectangle of thick paper in half. Then, draw a holster against the fold, like this. Keeping the paper folded, cut out the shape.

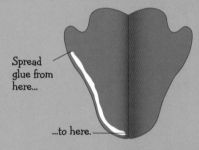

Spread glue from here...

...to here.

8. Open the holster. Spread a line of glue along one of the edges, down to the fold. Fold the holster again and carefully press the edges together.

9. Cut a thin paper strip with curved ends and fold it over the top of the holster. Glue one end onto the back of the holster and one onto the front.

Use the ideas on this page to make belts with different buckles.

Slot it so that the ends are inside the belt.

Glue the holster on this side of the buckle.

10. Glue the holster onto the belt. Then, use a brown felt-tip pen to draw patterns on the holster and belt. Add studs and metal details with a gold pen.

11. Make a cut halfway down into the belt at one end. Make a cut going halfway up into the belt at the other end. Slot the ends together to fasten the belt.

Frankenstein's monster mask

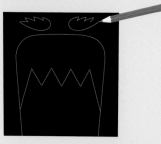

1. For the headband, cut a strip of thin cardboard that fits once around your head, with a little overlap. Overlap the ends and secure them with sticky tape.

Make the green shape as wide as your face.

2. Draw a large shape for the monster's forehead on thin green cardboard. Cut it out, lay it on a piece of thin black cardboard and draw around it.

3. Lift off the green shape. Then, draw a zigzag for hair inside the outline on the black cardboard. Add two bushy eyebrows. Cut out the hair and eyebrows.

To make a Dracula mask, draw a point in the middle of the hair, and add pointed ears instead of bolts.

4. Glue the hair onto the green shape. Glue the eyebrows at the bottom, overlapping the edge. Then, draw two curving wrinkles with a dark green pen.

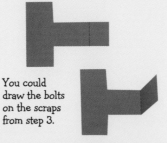

You could draw the bolts on the scraps from step 3.

5. Draw two chunky T-shaped bolts on a piece of thin dark cardboard. Cut them both out, then fold over the end of each bolt to make a tab, like this.

To wear your mask, slide it on until the headband is resting just above your ears.

6. Lay the mask face down. Spread a line of glue along the bottom edge, then press the headband onto it. Glue the bolts onto the headband, too.

Castle tower

Dip the eraser in the paint again and again.

1. Cut a big rectangle from thin cardboard. Spread paint on an old plate. Dip an eraser in the paint and use it to print 'bricks' on the cardboard.

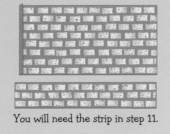

You will need the strip in step 11.

2. When the paint is dry, cut a strip from the rectangle and put it to the side. Then, fold over one edge of the big rectangle, to make a tab.

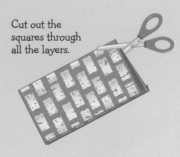

Cut out the squares through all the layers.

3. Keeping the tab folded, fold the rectangle in half, then in half again. Draw two squares on the top edge of the rectangle, then cut them out.

Draw the tabs at the bottom of the drawbridge.

4. Unfold the castle. Cut an arch from the third section and lay it on a piece of paper. Draw a drawbridge around the arch and add two tabs.

The tabs go on either side of the arch.

5. Carefully, cut out the drawbridge. Fold up the tabs and spread glue on them. Then, press the tabs onto the back of the castle, like this.

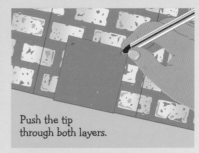

Push the tip through both layers.

6. Fold up the drawbridge. Then, push the tip of a ballpoint pen through the top corners of the drawbridge and through the castle wall.

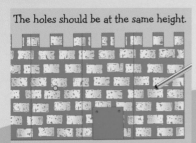

The holes should be at the same height.

7. Push a ballpoint pen all the way through the middle of the section to the left of the arch. Make a hole in the middle of the section on the right, too.

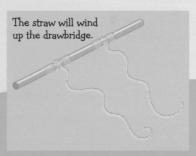

The straw will wind up the drawbridge.

8. Cut two long pieces of white thread, the same length. Tape one end of each piece onto a straw, leaving a space between them, like this.

You may need to tie each knot twice.

9. Push the threads through the holes in the front of the castle, then through the holes in the drawbridge. Tie a knot in the end of each thread.

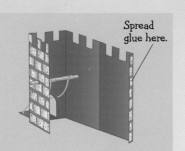

Spread glue here.

10. Bend the side walls around and push the straw through the side holes. Then, spread glue on the tab and bend the back around to make a square.

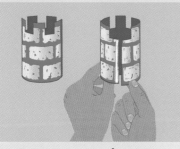

11. For turrets, cut the strip from step 2 in half. Cut squares into the top of each piece. Then, glue the ends of each piece together, like this.

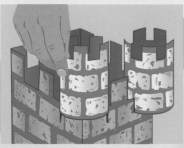

12. Cut a slit on either side of the front two corners of the rectangular tower. Then, carefully slot the two round turrets onto the castle.

You could cut flags and windows from paper and glue them onto the turrets.

Turn the straw to wind up the drawbridge.

Pirate hats

Rounded hat

 — Fold

1. Fold a large piece of black paper in half. With the fold at the top, lay a small plate on the paper, touching the bottom edge, like this.

2. Draw carefully around the plate. Then, draw curved lines going from either side of the circle to the edge of the paper, like this.

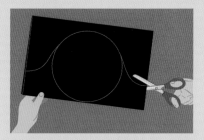

3. Holding the layers together, cut along the curved lines and around the top of the circle. Then, erase the remaining pencil line.

Glue the sides of the hat, but don't glue around the top.

4. Draw a skull and two bones on white paper. Cut them out and glue them onto one of the hat shapes. Then, glue the hat, like this.

Pointed hat

Fold

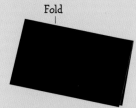

1. Fold a large piece of black paper in half. Crease the fold really well. Then, turn the paper, so that the fold is at the top, like this.

2. Bend the paper over so that the short edges meet. Gently squeeze the middle, like this, to make a mark. Then, open it out again.

Middle mark

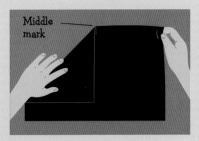

3. Fold the top left-hand corner down into the middle, then crease it down flat. Then, fold down the top right-hand corner, too.

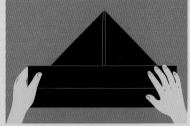

4. Fold up the top layer of paper at the bottom of the hat. Then, turn the hat over and fold the other layer in the same way.

Glue on the circle so that it secures the layers.

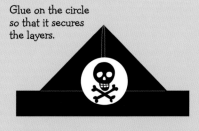

5. Cut a circle from white paper. Draw a skull with two crossed bones on the paper. Then, glue the circle onto the front of the hat.

If you're dressing up as
a pirate, wear a striped
T-shirt with your hat.

Find out how to make
an eye patch to wear
with your hat on page 93.

Corner kick drawing

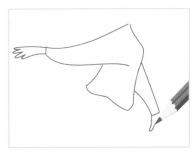

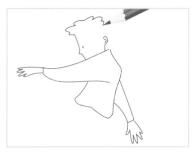

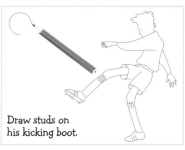

Draw studs on his kicking boot.

1. Pressing lightly with a pencil, draw a shape for a player's outstretched arm. Draw his body and his other arm, then draw both of his hands.

2. Draw a side-on face with a nose halfway down. Add an ear and a line for the back of the neck. Then, draw a dot for an eye and add some hair.

3. Draw the player's shorts, then add his legs, with one of them raised as if kicking a ball. Draw boots and socks, then add a ball up in the air.

You could draw two players, with one of them tackling to win the ball.

4. Draw a corner flag behind the player and add lines for the corner, starting at the bottom of the flag. Add a curve across the corner, too.

Draw all the lines in the same direction.

5. Outline the player and flag with a sharp black pencil. Then, using another pencil, fill in the player's face with lots of short diagonal lines.

The long lines will make it look as if the player is moving.

6. Fill in the hair. Then, draw lots of long lines down from the top arm, overlapping the black line. Fill in the player's shirt and other arm as well.

Add some movement lines around the ball, too.

7. Fill in the rest of the player and the flag. Outline the lines below the flag with a sharp green pencil. Add grass and 'whoosh' lines up to the ball.

Stand-up cattle

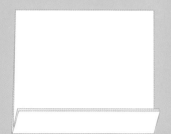

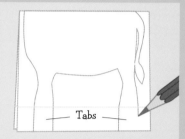

1. Fold a rectangle of thick white paper in half. Fold up the ends of the paper to make flaps. They will be the base of the cow. Then, unfold the flaps.

2. Draw a cow's body on the folded paper, with its back along the fold. Add lines coming down from the legs to the bottom of the flaps to make tabs.

3. Draw a cow's head on another piece of thick paper. Add horns, ears and a face. Fill in the head and make patches on the body using felt-tip pens.

Tabs

This cowboy was made with the top of his hat along the fold and the tabs below his heels.

Cut around the tabs.

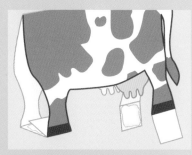

4. Cut out the head. Then, keeping the paper folded, cut out the cow's body, through both layers of paper. Don't cut along the cow's back.

5. For the base, fold the tabs under the body. Then, glue one tab on top of the other, like this. Press the tabs together until the glue sticks.

6. To attach the head, cut out a small square from thick cardboard and glue it onto the body, near the front. Glue the head onto the cardboard.

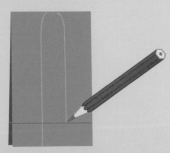

Don't cut along the fold.

7. For a cactus, fold a piece of green paper in half and make flaps, as you did in step 1. Then, draw a long, thin arch so that the top touches the fold.

8. Add branches on either side of the arch. Draw around the cactus with a green pen and add stripes. Hold the layers together and cut out the shape.

9. Fold both the tabs under the cactus. Then, glue one tab on top of the other one to make the base. Stand the cactus upright, like this.

You could make a herd of cattle and lots more cacti.

Roman soldier's sword

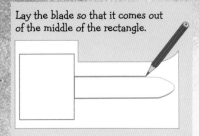

Lay the blade so that it comes out of the middle of the rectangle.

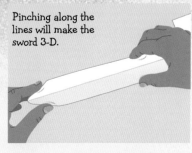

Pinching along the lines will make the sword 3-D.

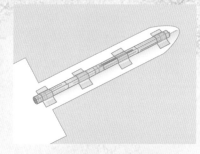

1. Draw a blade on thin cardboard, then cut it out. Draw a rectangle for a handle, then lay the blade next to it, like this, and draw around it.

2. Cut around the second shape. Pressing with a ballpoint pen, draw a line along the middle of each blade. Turn the blades over and pinch along the lines.

3. Cut a piece of newspaper as long as the blade. Roll the paper and secure it with tape. Tape it inside one of the blades, a little way below the tip.

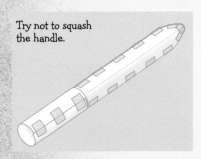

Try not to squash the handle.

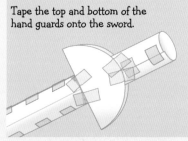

Tape the top and bottom of the hand guards onto the sword.

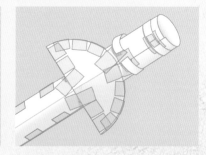

4. Lay the other blade on top so that the edges line up, then tape them together with sticky tape. Bend in the edges of the handle and tape them, too.

5. Draw around a big roll of sticky tape on cardboard and cut it out. Cut the circle in half to make two hand guards. Tape one onto each side of the sword.

6. Tape the edges of the hand guards together. Cut two thin cardboard strips and wrap them around the handle for grips. Secure them with sticky tape.

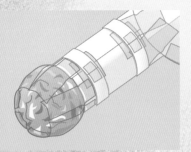

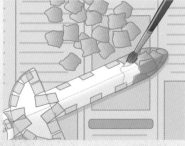

7. Cut a big square from kitchen foil, tightly scrunch it into a ball. Push the ball into the end of the handle and use sticky tape to hold it in place.

8. Rip lots of pieces of silver tissue paper. Mix a little water with white glue, then brush some onto the blade and press on pieces of silver paper.

9. Brush on more glue and press on paper until the blade is covered. Rip pieces of gold tissue paper, then glue them on the hand guards and handle.

The dagger above was made in the same way as the sword, then decorated with gold pen.

A Roman soldier's short sword was called a gladius. This kind of sword was used for stabbing and slashing at enemy soldiers.

Flying dragon

Start drawing on the right-hand side of your paper.

1. Draw a spiral for a dragon's nostril, then draw the top of the head. Add an oval eye, a horn and an ear. Then, draw the mouth with lots of teeth.

2. Add a curve for the dragon's back, then draw a big shape for the wing. Add another wing behind it. Then, draw the dragon's tummy underneath.

3. Draw curves for the back leg, and add a heel and three toes. Add claws on the toes and heel, then draw another leg behind the first one.

The knight will be here.

4. Draw a long, wavy tail. Draw a triangle on the tip of the tail, then draw lots of pointed scales all the way along the dragon's back and neck.

5. Add two curving lines for the dragon's arm. Then, draw a thumb and three fingers, with claws. Draw another arm behind the first one.

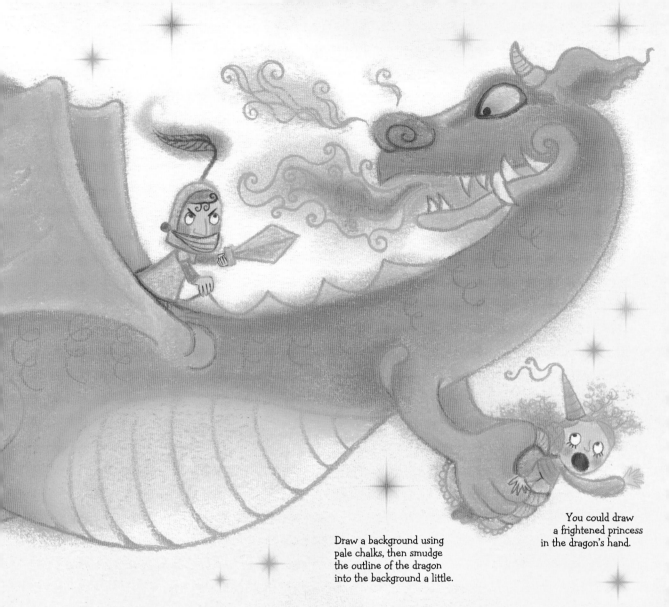

Draw a background using pale chalks, then smudge the outline of the dragon into the background a little.

You could draw a frightened princess in the dragon's hand.

Draw one arm holding a sword.

6. Draw a knight's body between the wings. Add a shape for the helmet, then draw the face. Draw the arms and add a sword, too.

7. Draw over the pencil lines using bright pencils. Then, add fire coming out of the dragon's mouth and smoke from the nostril.

8. Use bright shades of chalks or chalk pastels to fill in your drawing. Then, use your finger to smudge the chalks together a little.

Treasure chest

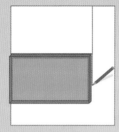

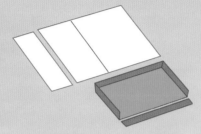

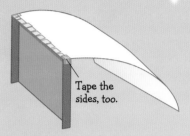

Tape the sides, too.

1. For the top of the chest, lay the lid of a shoe box on a large piece of thin cardboard. Then, carefully draw around it twice, like this.

2. Carefully, cut around the shape, then cut a strip off one end. Then, cut one of the longer sides off the lid of the shoe box.

3. Tape one of the short edges of the cardboard along the long side of the lid, like this, using lots of small pieces of sticky tape.

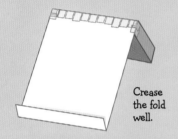

Crease the fold well.

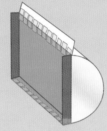

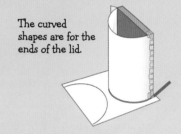

The curved shapes are for the ends of the lid.

4. Fold up the edge of the cardboard that hasn't been taped to the lid. The folded part will be used to make the hinge.

5. To make the top curve, tape the folded edge of the hinge to the lid, like this. Secure it with lots of small pieces of sticky tape.

6. Place one end of the lid at the edge of a piece of cardboard. Draw around the curve. Move the lid to the other edge and draw around it again.

Don't tape the hinge.

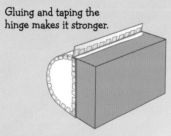

Gluing and taping the hinge makes it stronger.

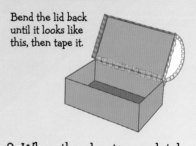

Bend the lid back until it looks like this, then tape it.

7. Cut out the curved shapes. Then, tape one shape onto each end of the lid, like this, matching the edges as neatly as you can.

8. Put the lid on the chest. Spread white glue all along the edge of the chest, then press down the hinge and tape it, too.

9. When the glue is completely dry, gently open the lid of the chest. Then, tape all the way along the hinge, inside the chest.

Put the chest on
a newspaper.

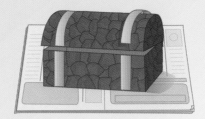

10. Rip lots of tissue paper into large pieces. Brush glue onto the chest and press on the pieces of tissue paper, until it is covered.

11. For straps, cut two strips of paper, and glue them onto the front of the chest. Then, glue two longer strips onto the lid, like this.

12. Draw one lock and two hinge shapes on shiny paper. Carefully cut them out and glue them onto the front and back of the chest.

Fill your treasure chest with coins (see page 26), jewels and other shiny treasure.

Saloon-door card

These flaps will make the saloon doors.

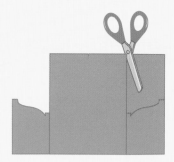

1. Bend a rectangle of thick brown paper in half and pinch the middle. Lay it flat, then fold over each end to meet the pinch. Crease the folds well.

2. Draw a curved line for the top of a door about halfway up one of the flaps. Draw a door on the other flap, too, making sure the doors are level.

3. Cut down the creases on both flaps. Then, carefully cut along the top of both of the doors so that you cut off the section above the lines.

Write your message on the back of the saloon doors.

76

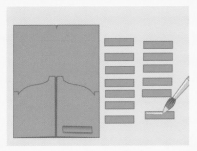

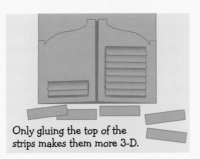

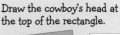
Draw the cowboy's head at the top of the rectangle.

4. Cut a long, thin strip from brown paper and cut it into little pieces. Brush glue along the top of one piece and glue it near the bottom of one door.

5. Brush a line of glue across the top of another piece and glue it above the first one, overlapping it slightly. Glue the pieces on both doors, like this.

6. Lay the card on a piece of white paper and draw around it. Cut out the rectangle. Then, draw a cowboy's head and add a face and hat.

7. Draw the cowboy's body and legs. Add a shirt, bandana, belt and boots. Paint the cowboy using thick paint, then paint the background black.

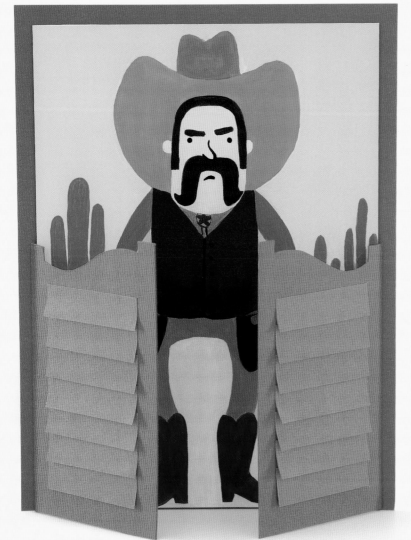

Glue the card along the bottom of the larger piece of cardboard.

8. When the paint is dry, open the doors and glue the paper onto the card. Glue the card onto a bigger piece of cardboard. Cut around it to make a doorframe.

Knight's helmet

1. For the jaw piece, cut a very long, wide strip of thin cardboard. The strip should go around your head, so that it covers your nose.

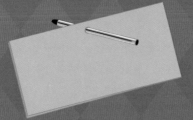

2. Fold the strip in half. Push a ballpoint pen through the cardboard, halfway along the strip, near the top. Make a hole in the other side, too.

3. Draw two curves on the cardboard, like this. Then, keeping the strip folded, cut along the lines. Bend the strip around and tape the ends.

This silver helmet had textured foil glued onto the cardboard for the strips and visor.

The helmet below had decorations drawn on the visor and jaw piece before it was put together.

A visor protected a knight's eyes but it also stopped him from seeing much!

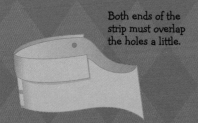

Both ends of the
strip must overlap
the holes a little.

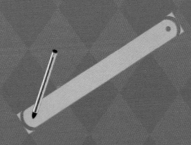

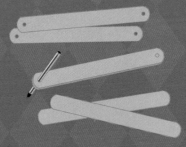

4. Cut a strip of cardboard. The strip must go around the back of the jaw piece, so the ends of the strip overlap the holes a little.

5. Carefully, cut the ends of the strip into curves. Draw a dot a little way in from each end, then push a ballpoint pen through each dot.

6. Draw around the shape five times on thin cardboard. Cut out the shapes, then make holes in the ends of each one using the first strip as a guide.

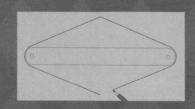

The hinges hold the helmet together and let the visor move up and down.

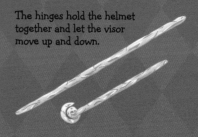

7. For the visor, draw around one of the strips. Add wide triangles above and below the shape. Then, cut it out and make holes in the ends.

8. Draw six rectangles with slanted ends on the visor. Pinch the middle of one and cut into it, then cut out the shape. Cut out all the shapes.

9. For the visor's hinges, cut two strips of foil twice as long as your middle finger. Roll them into sticks, then twist one end of each into a thick spiral.

The spirals should be inside the helmet.

You only need to tape the middle of each strip.

10. Push the sticks through the holes in the jaw piece. Thread a strip onto the sticks and move it until it overlaps the back of the jaw piece.

11. Tape the strip onto the jaw piece. Add another strip that overlaps the first one and tape it in place. Add all the strips in the same way.

12. Add the visor last, but don't tape it onto a strip, so it can move up and down. Twist the loose ends of the foil sticks into tight spirals.

Monster mouth bag

  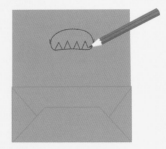

1. Draw a line across a paper carrier bag, below the bottom of the handles. Then, cut along the line to make two pieces. You don't need the top piece.

2. To make a new handle, place one hand near the top of the bag, with your fingers together. Draw a little mark on either side of your hand.

3. Draw a curved shape for a monster's mouth, using the little pencil marks as the ends of the mouth. Add pointed teeth along the bottom edge of the mouth.

Put your hand through the monster's mouth to carry the bag.

You could draw part of a toothy skeleton on a bag.

4. Before you draw the rest of the monster, fold the flap at the bottom of the bag to the back. Then, draw an arch over the mouth for the monster's head.

5. Draw a curved arm on each side of the monster, then add lots of tentacles at the bottom. Draw three round eyes above the mouth, too.

6. To make a hole for the handle, very carefully push the point of a sharp pencil through the middle of the mouth. Push it through both layers of the bag.

Monsters don't have to have teeth – try drawing a scary ghost with a gaping mouth instead.

7. Push one blade of a pair of scissors through the hole. Then, holding both layers of the bag together, carefully cut around the monster's mouth.

You could paint spots on your monster.

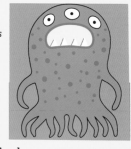

8. Lay the bag on a newspaper, then fill in the monster with thick paints. When the paint is dry, outline the monster with a black pen. Draw around his eyes.

Sheriff's badge

1. Draw a triangle on a piece of thin cardboard. Then, draw an upside-down triangle overlapping the first one to make a star. Cut out the shape.

2. Spread glue on the star and lay it sticky-side down on some kitchen foil. Cut around the star leaving a border, then fold the foil over the edges.

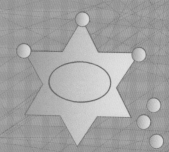

3. Cut an oval and six small circles from cardboard. Cover them with foil. Glue the oval onto the middle of the star, and the circles onto the points.

4. Press the tip of a blunt pencil into the foil to make a dotted pattern around the badge. Then, write the word 'SHERIFF' across the oval in the middle.

5. Turn the badge over. Open a paperclip out a little, then tape one side of it to the back of the badge, like this. Hook the paperclip onto your clothes.

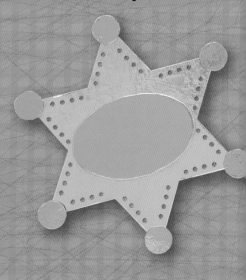

You could make a deputy's badge.

To make a gold badge like the one above, use the foil from a chocolate wrapper.

Jolly Roger paper

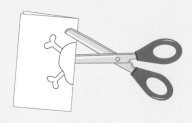

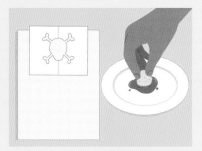

1. To make a stencil, fold some thick paper in half. Draw half a skull and two bones along the fold and then carefully cut along the lines.

2. Open out the stencil and lay it flat on a piece of paper. Spread some red paint on an old plate, then dip a sponge into the paint.

3. Dab paint all over the hole, then lift off the stencil. When the paint is completely dry, draw eyes, a small nose and a toothy grin on the skull.

You could decorate wrapping paper, gift tags and envelopes.

To Jolly Jake,

Ahoy there! I'm having a swashbuckling Pirate Party on Friday. Hope to see you there - don't forget your parrot...

From

Buccaneer Bob

You could make writing paper look old (see steps 1-3 on page 10).

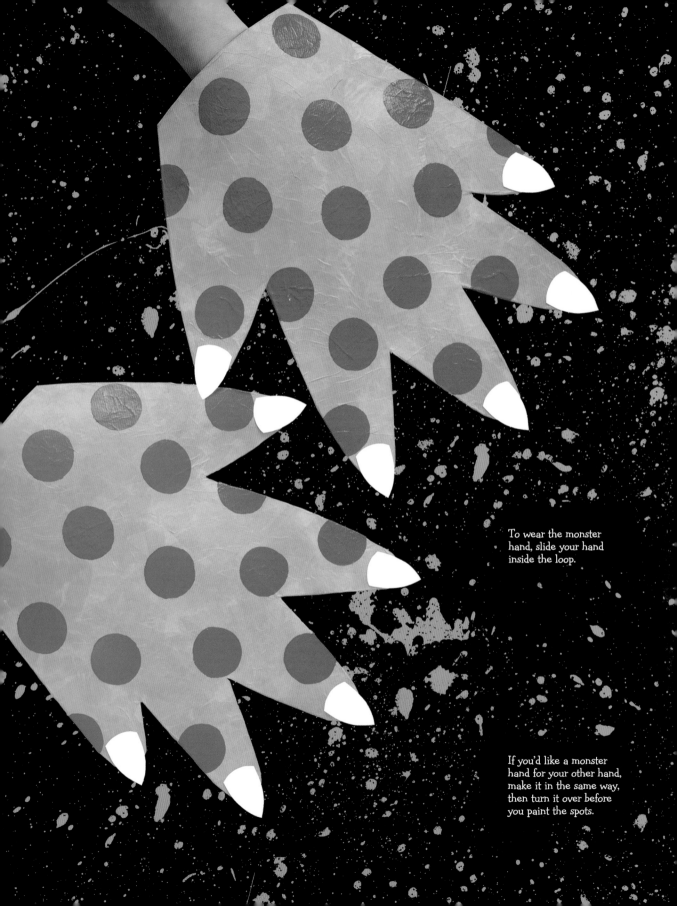

To wear the monster
hand, slide your hand
inside the loop.

If you'd like a monster
hand for your other hand,
make it in the same way,
then turn it over before
you paint the spots.

Monster hand

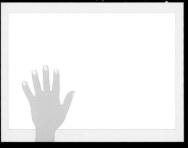

1. Lay your hand over the edge of a large piece of thin cardboard. The edge of the cardboard needs to be level with your wrist.

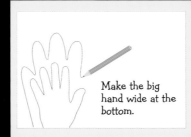

Make the big hand wide at the bottom.

2. Carefully draw around your hand with a pencil. Then, draw a much bigger, wider hand around the outline you have just drawn.

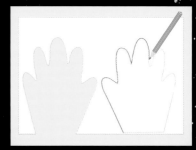

3. Cut out the big hand, then turn it over and lay it back on the cardboard, like this. Draw around it, then cut out the second shape.

Don't wrap it around too tightly.

4. Cut a strip of cardboard that will wrap once around your hand, with a small overlap. Then, tape the end down to make a loop, like this.

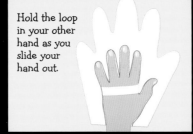

Hold the loop in your other hand as you slide your hand out.

5. Lay your hand inside the outline on the first big hand, then slide it out of the loop. Tape the loop onto the cardboard hand.

Try not to squash the loop inside.

6. Lay the other cardboard hand on top. Lining up the edges as well as you can, tape them together, but leave the bottom part open.

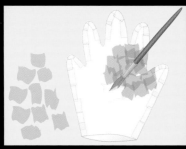

7. Rip lots of little pieces of green tissue paper. Then, brush white glue on part of the hand and press on the pieces of tissue paper.

8. Brush on more glue and press on more tissue paper until the hand is covered. When the glue is dry, paint pink spots all over the hand.

9. Leave the paint to dry. Cut five pointy fingernails from white cardboard. Glue one nail onto the end of each finger, like this.

Playing in the park

Make one leg look as if it is stretching out, like this.

Draw blobs for the hands – you will add fingers in step 6.

1. Use a bright chalk or chalk pastel to draw a shirt on a piece of green paper. Then, add a curved neckline with a white chalk.

2. Draw shorts with the white chalk, then add stripes with the bright chalk. Leave a gap for legs below the shorts, then draw shapes for socks.

3. Using a pale or darker brown chalk, draw a circle for the player's head, and add a neck below it. Then, draw the arms, hands and legs.

You could draw lots of players in different positions. Look at the sports pages of newspapers for ideas.

4. Draw the player's hair, then draw white ovals for boots. Using black and white chalks, draw a ball a little way above one of the player's boots.

5. Draw around the shirt with a thin black pen and then add a circle as a logo. Draw around the head, hair and neck, then draw a face, too.

6. Outline the arms, shorts, legs, socks and boots. Draw around the ball, then draw two movement lines below the ball with the white chalk.

You could draw two players heading the ball to each other.

You could draw a player dribbling a ball in and out of a line of markers.

Castle at night

The paints will bleed together.

1. Brush dark blue watery paint all over a piece of thick paper. While the paper is wet, brush stripes of purple paint on top. Leave the paint to dry.

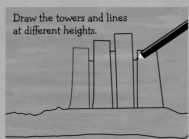

Draw the towers and lines at different heights.

2. Use a black pen to draw some land near the bottom of the paper. Then, draw four towers on one side. Add lines in between the towers.

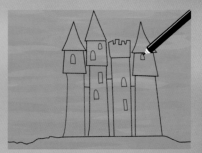

3. Add turrets and pointed roofs on top of three of the towers, and battlements on top of the other one. Draw some windows in the towers, too.

4. Fill in the land and castle using thick black paint, taking care not to paint over any of the windows. Then, leave the paint to dry.

Draw flags on some of the spires.

5. Use a black felt-tip pen to draw wintry trees and grass on the land. Then, add details on the castle such as window frames and spires.

Draw lots of lines for the moon's reflection.

6. Draw a moon using white chalk. Add white shading along one side of each tower. Then, draw wavy lines on the land and in the water.

You could draw a knight galloping across the land.

These birds were
drawn with a
black felt-tip pen.

Pop-up monster card

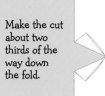

Make the cut about two thirds of the way down the fold.

1. Cut two rectangles of paper the same size, one white and the other yellow. Fold them both in half, with the short ends together.

2. Make a cut into the fold in the white rectangle, for the monster's mouth. Fold back the paper on each side of the cut, like this.

3. Turn the card over and fold the flaps back on themselves. Then, unfold the flaps, so that the card lies flat again.

If you make the cut a third of the way down the fold in step 2, you can draw a whole monster.

Write a message around your monster or on the back of the card.

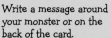

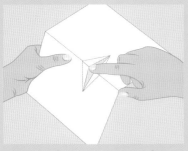

4. Open the card a little, then push the flaps down through the fold, like this. Close the card and press the folds to flatten them.

Glue the teeth to the back of the flaps.

5. Open the card. Draw a monster around the mouth, then fill it in with felt-tip pens. Cut teeth from paper and glue them on.

Line up the folds.

6. Cut around the monster. Then, spread glue all over the back of it, except for the mouth. Press it firmly onto the yellow rectangle.

You could make a monster with lots of teeth.

Pirate paraphernalia

Telescope

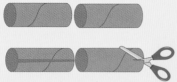

Use the cardboard tubes from inside rolls of paper towels.

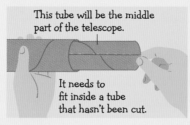

This tube will be the middle part of the telescope.

It needs to fit inside a tube that hasn't been cut.

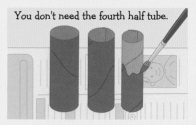

You don't need the fourth half tube.

1. Very carefully, cut two cardboard tubes in half with a bread knife. Then, cut two of these pieces from end to end with scissors.

2. Spread glue next to the cut edge of one of the half tubes. Overlap both sides of the cut and hold them together tightly, like this.

3. Glue the edge of the other sliced tube. Overlap its edges, until it fits inside the middle part. When it is completely dry, paint the tubes.

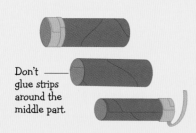

Don't glue strips around the middle part.

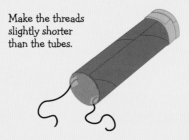

Make the threads slightly shorter than the tubes.

4. Cut a strip of cardboard. Glue it around one end of the widest tube, then glue a thin strip on top. Then, do the same with the narrow tube.

5. To hold the three parts of the telescope together, cut four pieces of thread. Tape two of the pieces inside the narrow tube, like this.

6. Slide the narrow tube inside the middle one. Then, carefully tape the loose ends of the threads inside the end of the middle tube.

Gently pull the ends of the telescope, to open it out.

7. Tape the other two pieces of thread inside the middle tube. Slide it inside the widest one, then secure the ends of the threads with sticky tape.

Shiny earring

The piece of foil secures the ends.

This part loops over your ear.

1. Cut a piece of foil that is about the size of a postcard. Squeeze it in your fingers, then roll it on a flat surface to make a thin stick.

2. Bend the stick into a circle, then twist the ends together. Wrap a small piece of foil around the part where the ends join.

3. Lay the earring over a thin rubber band that will go around your ear. Push one end of the rubber band through the other to make a loop.

Eye patch

Make the patch big enough to cover one of your eyes.

Tie the thread around your head.

1. Draw an eye patch on black paper, then cut it out. Make a cut into it, then spread glue next to the cut. Overlap the edges and hold them together.

2. Cut a piece of thread that will go around your head, plus some extra for tying it on. Tape it to the back of the eye patch, like this.

You could glue cardboard shapes onto your telescope.

You could make some ship's rats using brown cardboard, white paper, felt-tip pens and string.

Catapult

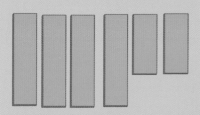

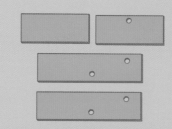

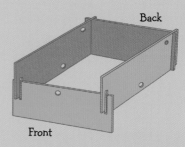

Back

Front

1. Cut four strips about 15cm (6in) long from thick cardboard. Then, cut two shorter strips that are the same width. Put two of the long strips to the side.

2. Use a hole puncher to make holes in three of the strips, like this. Make sure that the holes in the long strips are in the same place on each strip.

3. Make two cuts halfway down into each short strip, near the end. Then, make two cuts up into the long strips. Slot the strips together in a rectangle.

Use a pencil to make the holes bigger if you need to.

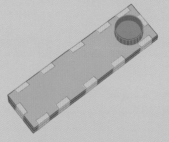

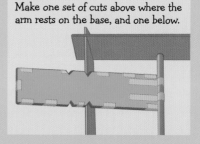

Make one set of cuts above where the arm rests on the base, and one below.

4. Cut a straw so it is a little wider than the base. Push it through the holes in the middle of the long sides. Slide a pipe cleaner in and twist the ends.

5. To make the arm, lay the two long strips from step 1 on top of each other and tape them together. Glue a clean bottle top near one end of the arm.

6. With the lid at the top and facing the front, tape the arm onto the straw. Rest the arm on the front of the base and make four cuts, two on either side.

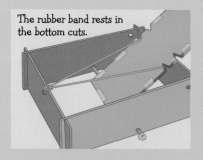

The rubber band rests in the bottom cuts.

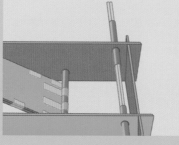

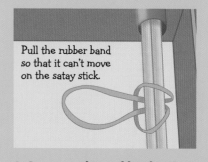

Pull the rubber band so that it can't move on the satay stick.

7. Push a 9cm (3½in) rubber band through the hole in the front of the base to make a loop. Pull the end through the loop and hook it onto the arm.

8. Cut two pieces from a straw and push the pieces through the holes at the back of the base. Then, slide two satay or kebab sticks through the straws.

9. Loop another rubber band around the satay sticks. Push one end through the loop and pull it very tight. Hook it over the top cuts in the arm.

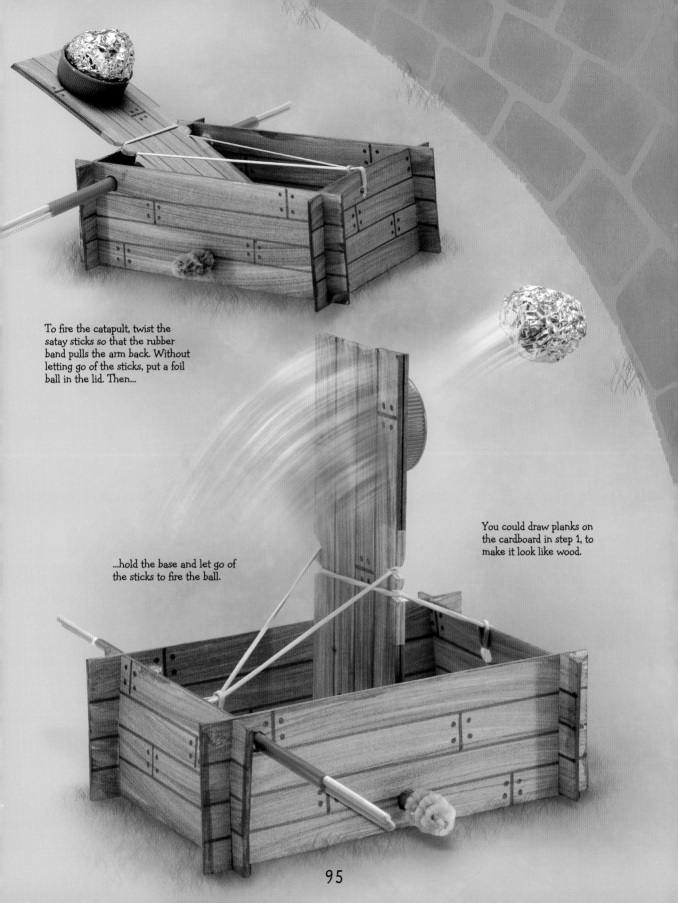

To fire the catapult, twist the satay sticks so that the rubber band pulls the arm back. Without letting go of the sticks, put a foil ball in the lid. Then...

...hold the base and let go of the sticks to fire the ball.

You could draw planks on the cardboard in step 1, to make it look like wood.

95

Index

Acknowledgements

Additional design and illustration by Samantha Barrett, Katrina Fearn, Non Figg,
Katie Lovell, Jan McCafferty and Antonia Miller.
Photographic manipulation by Will Dawes, John Russell and Nick Wakeford

First published in 2009 by Usborne Publishing Limited., 83-85 Saffron Hill, London, EC1N 8RT, England
www.usborne.com